TOWER HAMLETS

KT-404-326

91 000 004 125 83 7

NORMAN WHITNEY

Sara Says No!

idea

Library Learning Information

To renew this item call:

0115 929 3388

or visit

www.ideastore.co.uk

TOWER HAMLETS

Created and managed by Tower Hamlets Council

TOWER HAMLETS LIBRARIES	
91000004125837	
Bertrams	24/10/2013
	£4.10
THISBO	TH13001117

Welcome to Middletown! It is Monday morning. Everybody is at the market. The market is busy.

Today, there is a new man at the market. His name is Mister Fruit. His daughter is helping him. Her name is Sara.

'Good morning,' Mister Fruit says to everybody. 'My fruit is fresh. My fruit is cheap.'

Mister Fruit is polite. He is friendly. Everybody likes Mister Fruit. 'What a nice man!' they say. Everybody likes his daughter. 'What a nice girl,' they say.

A schoolboy asks for one kilo of apples.

Mister Fruit puts some apples on the scales. The scales show one kilo and one hundred grammes.

Mister Fruit takes one apple away. Now the scales show nine hundred grammes.

But Mister Fruit says, 'One kilo of apples! One dollar!' He takes one dollar from the schoolboy.

Sara is watching her father. She sees everything.

A young woman asks for two kilos of oranges.

Mister Fruit puts some oranges on the scales. The scales show two kilos and two hundred grammes.

Mister Fruit takes one orange away. Now the scales show one kilo and eight hundred grammes.

But Mister Fruit says, 'Two kilos of oranges. Two dollars!' He takes two dollars from the young woman.

Sara sees everything.

It is Monday evening. Sara's father is counting his money. He is happy. But Sara is not happy. She is angry.

Father! You must sell the correct weight. You mustn't cheat our customers. Our customers are poor.

But we are poor too, Sara! My wife is dead. You have no mother. I have no sons. You have no brothers. We must make money, Sara! That's life!

I don't want to work at the market, father.

You must work at the market! We must live, Sara. We must eat! You're a child. You don't understand business. You're a woman. Women don't understand business. That's life, Sara!

7

It is Tuesday morning. Today, Sara's father is selling the correct weight. He is honest. He takes the correct money.

Sara is happy. Today, she is proud of her father.

The customers are happy too. They buy a lot of fruit. 'Your fruit is cheap and fresh,' they say.

But in the afternoon, some customers come back. They are angry.

An old man brings back some apples. One of his apples is bad. A girl brings back some oranges. One of her oranges is bad. A woman brings back some bananas. One of her bananas is bad. It is black, and full of worms.

'Look, Mister Fruit! Your fruit isn't fresh today. We want our money back!'

But Mister Fruit does not listen. He does not give them any money.

'You're dishonest, father!' says Sara. 'You're cheating the customers! I don't want to work for you. I don't want to work at the market!'

'But you must work for me, Sara,' says her father. 'I have no family! I have no wife, and no sons. Children must help their parents. You are my daughter, Sara. You must work for me. That's life!'

'No, father,' says Sara. 'I don't want to clean your house. I want to leave home. I don't want to cook your food. I want to get a good job! I'm not going to work for you.'

Sara's father is angry. 'Go to bed!' he shouts at her.

Sara goes to bed. She is lonely. She is unhappy. She says a prayer.

It is Wednesday morning. Everybody is at the market. Everybody is laughing. Something strange is happening.

Mister Fruit touches an apple. The apple goes bad. Then he picks up an orange. The orange goes bad too. Then he picks up some bananas. They go black.

Everybody laughs. 'Look at Mister Fruit! He touches the fruit and it goes bad!'

Mister Fruit looks at his hands. 'What is happening?' he says. 'Please, Sara. Please help me.'

Sara touches an apple. She picks up an orange and some bananas.

'Hooray!' everybody says. 'It's a miracle! Sara touches the fruit and it's OK! We're going to buy our fruit from Sara!'

Next year, Mister Fruit is Miss Fruit.

Sara is honest. She does not cheat. She always sells the correct weight. She sells good, fresh fruit. She understands business.

Sara is making a lot of money. She has a good job now.

Sara's father stays at home. He cleans the house. He cooks the food. He is very happy! 'That's life!' he says.